Musicianship in Practice

Book I: Grades 1–3

This material has been prepared primarily to offer guidance
for ABRSM's Practical Musicianship exams. It is hoped that
music teachers will find in it a useful basis on which to plan
a scheme of study in this important aspect of musical learning.

Where appropriate a background note has been given showing
the purpose of the test, and in some cases a preliminary exercise
has been suggested before attempting the specimen tests.
It should be noted that in most cases ample practice material
will be found in the music that pupils are currently learning.
This should be used whenever possible to emphasize the relevance
of practical musicianship as an aid to performance.

ABRSM

Published by ABRSM (Publishing) Ltd, a wholly owned subsidiary of ABRSM
Printed on materials from sustainable sources

Test 1A: Rhythm tapping

This test is designed to develop alertness of response to the rhythm of a phrase. Each response starts on a strong beat, and the pupil should take care not to anticipate this. As a preliminary exercise, the teacher could tap two-bar patterns for the pupil to echo without a pause so that the flow of the rhythm is continuous. The examination test will be eight bars long, containing two required responses. Some exercises of sixteen bars (four phrases) are included below for practice purposes.

PRACTICE EXERCISES

SPECIMEN TESTS

'To tap, as an echo, the rhythm pattern of two two-bar phrases in simple time played by the examiner. The echoes should follow each phrase in strict time without an intervening pause.'

Test 1B: Echo singing

As in Test 1A, alertness of response should be the aim. Here again the pupil should take care not to anticipate the strong beat at the start of each response. The exercises should be played with well-marked rhythmic accentuation. It may be helpful to prepare for this test by playing two-bar figures, so that the pupil can practise how to remember and pitch the starting note of each. The examination test will be eight bars long, containing two required responses. Some exercises of sixteen bars (four phrases) are included below for practice purposes.

PRACTICE EXERCISES

SPECIMEN TESTS

'To sing, as an echo, two two-bar phrases in simple time played by the examiner. The echoes should follow each phrase in strict time without an intervening pause.'

Test 1C: Playing from memory

The ability to play from memory is a valuable asset for all instrumentalists (note that singers will need to perform on a piano or any other instrument of their choice which they should bring with them – possibly a small chromatic glockenspiel). Two-bar phrases, based on stepwise movement and triad shapes, are used. The pupil should start by visualising the shape of the melody, singing it in the early stages to ensure correct memorisation before trying to imagine what it will feel like under the hand(s). It may be helpful to allow a pupil a trial attempt after two hearings, and then to play a third time in order to finalize the response. The examiner will take care to choose a test with a suitable key for transposing instruments. A mixture of keys is given here which should meet the needs of the various instruments. As preliminary exercises, the shapes of shortened scales and triads could be used, and so could the playing from memory of well-known tunes in suitably easy keys. Appropriate two-bar melodies taken from Tests 1A and 1B may also be used for practice purposes.

PRACTICE EXERCISES

SPECIMEN TESTS
'To play from memory on an instrument chosen by the candidate a two-bar melody played twice by the examiner. The key-chord will be sounded and the starting note appropriate to the candidate's instrument will be named.'

Test 1D: Sight singing

The skill of singing at sight is particularly useful for all musicians, and not just for singers. The test concentrates on scale patterns and primary triad shapes. As a start, it would be helpful for the pupil to sing the rhythm on a monotone (say to 'lah', though some may prefer to use French time names), and to practise pitching notes of the primary triads. The pupil should then be encouraged to look for tonic notes and to see the patterns of the other notes in relation to them. Suitable practice material may be found in traditional and popular songs with a strong tonal quality. Examples taken from Tests 1B and 1C may also be used for practice purposes.

SPECIMEN TESTS
'To sing at sight a four-bar melody in 2/4 time to a simple accompaniment played by the examiner. The key-chord and starting note will first be sounded and named, and the pulse indicated.'

Test 1E: Improvising

A creative sense needs to be developed in all pupils, and to help achieve this the improvisation of an answering phrase is a good starting point. In this test it is important that rhythmic continuity and balance are preserved, and that the phrase should aim for the final tonic (best approached by step from above or below). For a pupil new to this kind of study, it would be helpful to tap a rhythm in response before attempting a melody. The pupil could subsequently practise playing (or singing) an answering phrase by repeating the first bar and simply adding a tonic note in the final bar. All that would remain would be to try and achieve fluency with a more interesting melodic shape. If the first attempt is unsuccessful, a second version should be tried.

Here are examples of poor and good answers, followed by specimen tests.

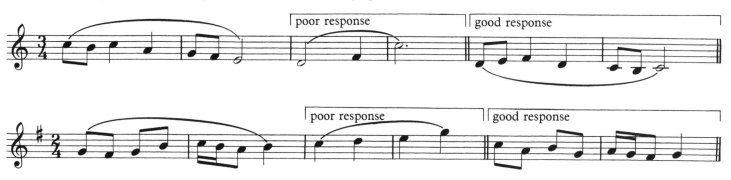

SPECIMEN TESTS

'To improvise with voice or instrument, at the choice of the candidate, a two-bar answering phrase to a two-bar phrase played by the examiner. The key-chord will first be sounded and the starting note of the given phrase appropriate to the candidate's voice or chosen instrument will be named. The answering phrase should follow in strict time after the examiner has played the opening phrase. A second attempt will be allowed.'

Test 1F: Noticing differences

The aim of this test is to develop a skill, essential to all musicians, of spotting a mistake in one's own performance or in that of others. The more a pupil is able to notice differences between what is printed and what is played, the better will be that pupil's ability to sight read. It is important to identify *where* a change occurs; credit will be given for this in the examination, even if the candidate cannot say precisely what the difference is. The changes at Grade 1 relate only to actual notes and their values, as the specimen tests below demonstrate. For further practice, a teacher may take any easy melody and make similar changes to it whilst the pupil follows the score.

SPECIMEN TESTS
'To recognize, from the printed score, the three or four changes made to pitch and note values in a melody played twice by the examiner. The candidate will be required to point to and explain the differences. The key-chord will be sounded before the melody is played.'

The small notation above the staves in the tests below indicates the differences in the pupil's copy.

12

Test 2A: Echo singing with an ostinato

Following on from Tests 1A and 1B in a combined form, this new test requires both alertness of response and the ability to co-ordinate independent rhythmic and melodic figures. It may be helpful for the pupil to begin by tapping a basic pulse in single beats before attempting to continue with a rhythmic ostinato. Here again each response starts on a strong beat, and the pupil should take care not to anticipate this. Here are two simple practice exercises, and teachers should devise similar ones before proceeding to the specimen tests.

PRACTICE EXERCISES

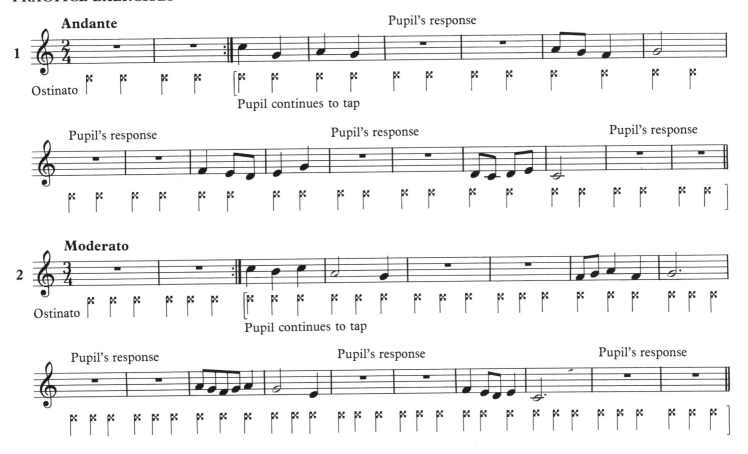

SPECIMEN TESTS

'To sing, as an echo, two two-bar phrases in simple time played by the examiner, whilst continuously tapping a repeated rhythm pattern (i.e. an ostinato) previously indicated by the examiner. The echoes should follow each phrase in strict time without an intervening pause.'

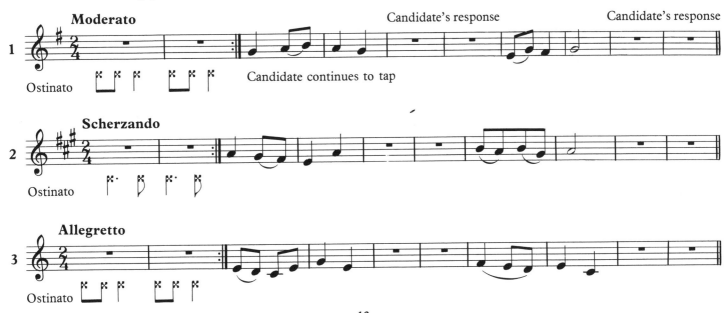

Test 2B: Playing from memory

The experience gained from Test 1C will prove of value in tackling these slightly harder examples. Here again the pupil should start by visualising the shape of the melody, singing it to confirm memorisation, and then feeling it under the hand(s). Once this has been achieved, it may be helpful to forget the memory part of the test whilst the pupil acquires familiarity on the instrument by playing well-known melodies in suitably easy keys. Appropriate two-bar melodies taken from Tests 1A, 1B and 1C may be used for supplementary practice in the early stages, and other practice material is given below.

PRACTICE EXERCISES

SPECIMEN TESTS

'To play from memory on an instrument chosen by the candidate a two-bar melody played twice by the examiner. The key-chord will first be sounded and the starting note appropriate to the candidate's instrument will be named.'

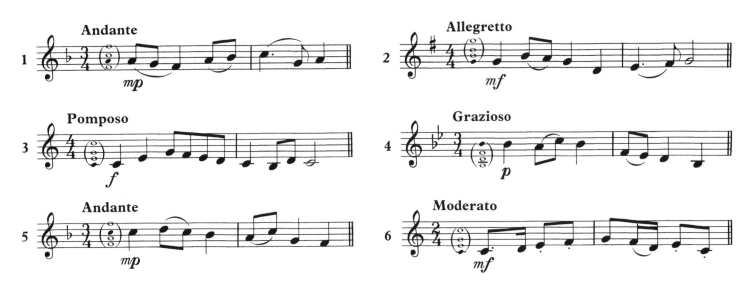

15

Test 2C: Sight singing

This test is a progressive step from Test 1D in developing the skill of singing at sight, essential to instrumentalists as well as to singers. In these harder examples the pupil should be encouraged to look for signposts such as tonic notes, cadence points and sequential patterns. Some independent rhythmic movement is incorporated, and so it would be useful for the pupil first to practise this by singing the rhythm on a monotone (say to 'lah' or French time names). Tapping the rhythm against the accompaniment would then prepare the pupil for the final version. Examples taken from Tests 1B, 1C, 1D and 2B may be used for supplementary practice material in the early stages.

SPECIMEN TESTS
'To sing at sight a four-bar melody in 2/4 or 3/4 time to a simple accompaniment played by the examiner. The key-chord and starting note will first be sounded and named, and the pulse indicated.'

16

5 Pomposo

6 Alla Valse

7 Andante tranquillo

8 Risoluto

Adagio

Andante espressivo

Moderato

Boldly

Test 2D: Improvising

The answering phrases in this test take the creative sense developed in Test 1E a stage further. Continuity of rhythm and balance are still important factors to bear in mind; likewise the ending of the phrase on the tonic and the need for the response to follow on rhythmically. If the first attempt is unsuccessful, a second version should be tried.

Here are examples of poor and good answers, followed by specimen tests.

SPECIMEN TESTS

'To improvise with voice or instrument, at the choice of the candidate, a two-bar answering phrase to a two-bar phrase played by the examiner. The key-chord will first be sounded and the starting note of the given phrase appropriate to the candidate's voice or chosen instrument will be named. The answering phrase should follow in strict time after the examiner has played the opening phrase. A second attempt will be allowed.'

Test 2E: Noticing differences

This Grade 2 test is similar to Test 1F in that the changes relate only to actual notes and their values, but the examples are a little harder. In the examination, examiners will highlight and repeat any of the changes which have given difficulty.

SPECIMEN TESTS
'To recognize, from the printed score, the three or four changes made to pitch and note values in a melody played twice by the examiner. The candidate will be required to point to and explain the differences. The key-chord will be sounded before the melody is played.'

The small notation above the staves in the tests below indicates the differences in the pupil's copy.

Test 3A: Echo singing with an ostinato

Somewhat harder than Test 2A, this Grade 3 test also calls for both alertness and co-ordination of the two aspects of response. It may be helpful for the pupil to begin by tapping a basic pulse in single beats before attempting to continue with a rhythmic ostinato. Here again each response starts on a strong beat, and the pupil should take care not to anticipate this.

SPECIMEN TESTS

'To sing, as an echo, two two-bar phrases in simple time played by the examiner, whilst continuously tapping a repeated rhythm pattern (i.e. an ostinato) previously indicated by the examiner. The echoes should follow each phrase in strict time without an intervening pause.'

Test 3B: Playing from memory

At Grade 3, this test includes a greater range of intervals than used previously. In addition to the practice suggestions mentioned in Test 2B, the pupil should therefore work on recognizing, singing and playing 6ths, 7ths and 8ves from memory. At this level the pupil will also be expected to maintain good playing habits and to achieve satisfactory tone, rhythm and phrasing. Consequently, it may be helpful to allow the pupil a trial attempt after two hearings. When the progression to playing more promptly has been accomplished, the melody can be played a third time in order to achieve a more musical result.

SPECIMEN TESTS
'To play from memory on an instrument chosen by the candidate a two-bar melody played twice by the examiner. The key-chord will first be sounded and the starting note appropriate to the candidate's instrument will be named.'

Test 3C: Sight singing

With the addition of 4/4 and 6/8 times, this test continues to develop the skill of sight singing. Besides actually singing the melodic line, the pupil will hopefully begin to hear the melody silently. As in Test 2C, the pupil should look for tonic notes, cadence points and sequential patterns, but gradually omit the practice of singing the rhythm on a monotone and tapping the rhythm with the accompaniment. Examples taken from Tests 2B and 2C may be used for supplementary practice in the early stages.

SPECIMEN TESTS
'To sing at sight a four-bar melody in 2/4, 3/4, 4/4 or 6/8 time to an accompaniment played by the examiner. The key-chord and starting note will first be sounded and named, and the pulse indicated.'

Test 3D: Improvising

At Grade 3, another step in the development of creative skills is taken with the introduction of four-bar phrases and responses. It is therefore all the more important to preserve rhythmic continuity and balance in order to prevent the melody from wandering aimlessly. An overall A-B-A-C pattern may be acceptable, but a better result would show some imagination in the first phrase of the response with, for example, skilful use of figures from the melody and rhythm, perhaps with inversion when appropriate.

Here are two examples, showing some of the possibilities.

SPECIMEN TESTS

'To improvise with voice or instrument, at the choice of the candidate, a four-bar answering phrase to a four-bar phrase played by the examiner. The key-chord will first be sounded and the starting note of the given phrase appropriate to the candidate's voice or chosen instrument will be named. The answering phrase should follow in strict time after the examiner has played the opening phrase. A second attempt will be allowed.'

Test 3E: Noticing differences

In this Grade 3 test, the examples are longer and more difficult, and there are two extra elements: rest values and the introduction of dynamic markings (these changes are quite distinct). As in Grade 2, examiners will highlight and repeat any of the changes which have given difficulty or which have been missed in the two playings.

SPECIMEN TESTS
'To recognize, from the printed score, the four changes made to pitch, note and rest values, and dynamics in a melody played twice by the examiner. The candidate will be required to point to and explain the differences. The key-chord will be sounded before the melody is played.'

The small notation and the dynamics in square brackets in the tests indicate the differences in the pupil's copy.

Processed and printed by
Halstan & Co. Ltd., Amersham, Bucks., England

This Fifi and the Flowertots
Annual 2011 belongs to

....

....

First published in the UK by HarperCollins Children's Books in 2010

13579108642
ISBN: 978-0-00-736592-0

© Chapman Entertainment Limited 2010

A CIP catalogue record for this title is available from the British Library.

Created by Keith Chapman
Based on the television series Fifi and the Flowertots, © Chapman Entertainment Limited 2010

Visit Fifi at www.Fifiandtheflowertots.com

Printed and bound in China.

Fifi and the Flowertots
Annual 2011

HarperCollins *Children's Books*

Hello! I'm Fifi Forget-Me-Not and I live in Flowertot Garden.
In this Annual, I'll be gardening, having a picnic and holding
a sleepover with all my friends. Would you like to come and play too?

Fifi x

Contents

Find the Friends

Fifi is playing hide and seek
with four of her friends.
Can you see them all?
Each time you find a Flowertot,
point to them and say
their name.

Harvest Time

It was a blustery winter's morning in Flowertot Garden. Fifi had a special reason to get up early today. It was time to harvest her vegetable patch.

"Brrrr!" she shivered, pulling back the bedcovers. "It's going to be chilly outside!"

Fifi tripped down the stairs to her little yellow kitchen, then made herself a cup of warm milk. She peeped out of the window to take a look at her vegetable garden. Fifi's carrots poked their heads out in neat rows and a mass of green cabbages swayed in the breeze.

The Tot got herself dressed in a trice.

"Fiddly flowerpetals!" she chuckled. "I'd better find my boots!"

Fifi pulled on her snuggly pink duffel coat, then headed out to the garden.

"Beep-beep!" honked Mo, revving up his engine.

Fifi gave the lawn mower a friendly good morning wave.

"Hello Mo!" she cried. "Lots to do today!"

The Flowertot walked up and down her garden, checking all of her vegetables. There were carrots, parsnips, cabbages and plump winter radishes. Before Fifi started picking, she reached for her broom.

"Better sweep the blowy leaves away first," she decided.

Just then Bumble buzzed down in front of her.

"I'll help you sweep, Fifi!" he smiled.

Bumble was a great help with the sweeping. The friends soon had the garden looking neat and tidy.

"Right-o!" cried the friendly bee. "Time for me to go home and rearrange my honeypots."

"Thank-you Bumble!" beamed Fifi.

When Bumble had gone, Fifi decided to start picking the carrots first.

She put her hands around the green leaves on top of the first carrot and tugged hard.

"Ooh!" gasped the Tot. "It's stuck!"

Fifi tried the next one and the one after that. Every single carrot was the same.

"Vroom!" chugged Mo.

"I know," sighed Fifi. "I'm going to need some more help."

Fifi listened for noises in the garden, but it seemed that everybody else was still in bed.

"If only Bumble was still here," she wished.

Suddenly there was a rustling in the bushes. Fifi grinned as Pip Gooseberry skidded into the garden on his scooter.

"Golly gooseberries!" he cried. "Look at those carrots!"

"They're ripe for picking," nodded Fifi. "Will you help me?"

Pip fetched a spade and got started. While he dug away at the soil, Fifi pulled at each carrot top. Before long they had a huge stack of yummy vegetables piled up at the side of the patch.

Fifi gave Pip a grateful hug. "You get home for breakfast, I can manage the rest."

Fifi picked up a big armful of cabbages and carried them over to Mo's trailer.

"Buttercups and daisies!" puffed the Tot. "This is hard work!"

"What are you doing?" asked Stingo, wandering up with Slugsy.

"I've picked my vegetables. Now I've just got to load all the harvest into Mo's trailer," explained Fifi.

Slugsy pointed at the giant veggie pile. "That's a lot to do all by yoursssself!"

The Tot nodded. "Will you give me a hand?"

Stingo grabbed Slugsy's belt and dragged him back towards Apple Tree House.

"Sorry Fifi!" he snapped. "It's too cold for us to waste time out here with you!"

But as soon as the poor Flowertot got back to work, the sneaky wasp snatched a few vegetables from the huge stack and hurried home. "It's only fair that Fifi shares them with us!" the naughty wasp explained to Slugsy.

It took Fifi all morning to get her vegetables picked and packed into Mo's trailer. The mower chugged slowly back to Fifi's house just as Primrose and Violet walked past.

"Would you like to warm up at ours with a cup of tea?" called Violet.

"Sorry, can't stop," replied Fifi. "I need to bring my vegetable harvest indoors."

Primrose and Violet watched as their friend lifted the first carrot out of Mo's trailer. It looked ever so heavy for one little Tot to manage all by herself.

"Bothering bluebells!" shouted Primrose. "You can't do that on your own. Come on Violet!"

Before Fifi could say anything, Primrose and Violet had lifted all the vegetables inside.

"That's better!" cried Primrose, heading home to wash the mud off her coat.

Fifi's kitchen was soon stacked high with lovely fresh vegetables.

"I think I'll make a nice winter soup with all these *yummy* vegetables," smiled Fifi. "Just the thing for this chilly weather."

Just then, Buttercup and Daisy popped their heads around the kitchen door.

"What are you making Fifi?" asked Daisy.

"Can we help?" wondered Buttercup.

The Tots got washing, stirring and chopping. Together, they made bowls and bowls of warming winter soup.

"We're running out of pots," cried Daisy a little later.

"Don't worry," said Buttercup. "We'll get some extra ones from our house."

The twins pulled on their coats, then raced out to fetch the pots for Fifi.

Stingo and Slugsy's cookery session was not going half as well as Fifi's.

"How do you cook vegetables anyway?" asked Stingo, shoving a parsnip at Slugsy.

"I dunno bosss!" moaned his pal. "I normally eat Diggly's spare peelings from the compost heap!"

"What about a carrot cake?" asked Stingo, cutting a carrot up and shoving it in a pan. "Let's make that!"

After half an hour of chopping, stirring and baking, Stingo and Slugsy were left with a frying pan full of sticky orange goo.

"This doesn't smell or even look like carrot cake," said Slugsy. "Yuk! It tastes horrible!"

Stingo threw down his wooden spoon. "I give up!"

"Look bosss," said Slugsy, pointing through the window. "The others are outside having fun!"

Fifi made enough soup to fill up all of her saucepans, plus Buttercup and Daisy's too.

"My, my," sighed the tired Flowertot. "What am I going to do with it all?"

Just then, Primrose and Bumble knocked on Fifi's front door.

"Look outside!" smiled Bumble. "It's started to snow!"

"I've been so busy I hadn't even noticed," gasped Fifi, putting her face up to the window pane.

"We can see that," remarked Primrose. "What a lot of soup!"

Fifi rubbed the window glass with the back of her hand. "Look! There are the twins and Pip, and Violet too!"

"Would you like to come out and play with us?" suggested Primrose to Fifi. "Everybody's asking for you."

Bumble looked outside. "The snowflakes do look pretty."

Fifi clapped her hands with excitement. "Let's go!" she giggled. "I'm all ready!"

While Fifi popped on her fluffy scarf and ear muffs, Violet knocked on the window.

"We're making a Snow-tot!" she beamed. "Come on Fifi!"

The Snow-tot was a sparkly, snowy sensation. All the friends clapped when it was finished. After that, the Flowertots enjoyed sledging, snowball games and an icicle hunt.

"We're getting ch-chilly!" shuddered Buttercup, at last.

"Can we go in Fifi?" asked Daisy.

Fifi's face lit up. She had just had a brilliant idea.

"Let's have a bowl of my fresh vegetable soup!" she announced.

"You have all helped me so much today. It's my way of saying thank-you."

"Yes please!" shouted Pip. "Sounds scrummy."

Stingo and Slugsy hung their heads sadly, as Pip and Fifi started to lead the others back into the warm.

"We didn't help you at all," wailed Slugsy. "Did we Fifi?"

Stingo walked up to Fifi, looking very sheepish.

"And I took some of your vegetables," he muttered. "But I won't do it again, wasp's honour!"

Luckily Fifi wasn't the kind of Tot to hold a grudge.

"I had plenty of vegetables to spare if you'd only asked," she smiled.

"You'll just have to help me now instead - by drinking up all this soup I've made!"

Before long all the Flowertots in Flowertot Garden were laughing at the story of Stingo's horrible carrot cake. Everybody agreed that Fifi's delicious soup recipe was much, much nicer.

"I couldn't have harvested those vegetables on my own," said Fifi. "And I couldn't have eaten them all on my own either!"

"Three cheers for Fifi!" shouted Bumble, raising his bowl in the air.

The Flowertot beamed at her dear friends. It had been a very good harvest indeed.

Market Maze

Fifi has been working hard in the garden, but her rake has broken! Can you help her find her way to Poppy's market stall to buy a new one?

Start

Finish

Lost and Found

Everyone's got mixed up! Can you match each
Flowertot to their favourite thing?

1. Cottonsocks

2. Grubby

B. Pip

A. Fifi

C. Aunt Tulip

3. Scooter

Dream Cakes

Yum yum! Fifi is about to cook a scrumptious cake.
Draw a picture of it in the space below.

Oh dear, Stingo and Slugsy are baking too. This time, draw the messiest, yuckiest-looking cake you can think of!

Singalong Fifi

Fifi is singing her song! Can you sing along
with her? The words are printed below.

Fifi and the Flowertots
Fifi Forget-Me-Not
Fifi, it's a lovely day

Fifi, who we love a lot
Fifi, little garden tot
Fifi, all your friends are here today

She sews
She grows
And everybody knows
It's Fifi
Fifi's world.

Jigsaw Feast

There's a piece missing from this picture of the Flowertots eating juicy tomatoes. Can you work out which one it is? Write your answer in the box below.

A.

B.

C.

Piece 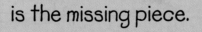 is the missing piece.

Join the Dots

Pip wants to have some fun! Can you join the dots
to make a swing for him to play on?

Fruity Wordsearch

Can you help Fifi find lots of tasty fruit
and vegetables in the word grid below?

b e a n s a i f d
b k z p y y o t p
l s u a t w h s b
a j b m w b i m e
m a p p l e o o r
l e b k t n s n
i b p i p u s v
j l w n b l b q e
t o m a t o e s s

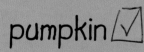 beans   tomatoes ✓ 4

pumpkin ✓ 2   onions ✓

apple ✓   berries ✓

Pretty as Primrose

Primrose loves to make herself look nice
and pretty. Do you like to dress up?
Here are some ideas for pretty things
you can make yourself to wear. Always
remember to get a grown-up to help.

Primrose's Pretty Pasta Necklace

You will need:
★ Dry pasta shapes
(like penne or macaroni)
★ Felt-tip pens or paint
★ Ribbon, string or sparkly thread

1. Paint the pasta using the felt-tips or paints.

2. Leave the shapes to dry.

3. Ask a grown-up to measure a piece of thread for the necklace and to cut it about 10cm longer than you need so there will be enough room to tie a knot in the end.

4. Choose enough coloured pasta pieces to make your necklace. Thread the ribbon or string through each piece.

5. Leave enough ribbon or string at each end so that you can tie a knot or bow!

6. Wear it to a party! You could also make a bracelet by using less thread and pasta.

ALWAYS ASK AN ADULT TO HELP YOU.

Colour Flutterby

Use your crayons to turn
Flutterby's wings blue and orange.
Then he'll fly you away to Flowertot Garden!

Slugsy's Mix-up

It's Stingo's birthday but silly Slugsy has brought the wrong things. Look at the pictures below and circle the items which don't belong at a birthday party.

A.

B.

C.

D.

E.

F.

G.

Bake with Bumble

Bumble's favourite food is honey. Sometimes he gives jars of honey to Fifi as a present so she can make yummy cakes. Why not make some honey choco crispy cakes as a special treat or to give to a friend?

Always ask a grown-up to help you.

You will need:

★ 100g (3.5oz) cocoa powder

★ 3 tbsp butter

★ 4 tbsp honey

★ 150g (5oz) crisped rice

★ Mixing bowl

★ Saucepan

★ Wooden spoon

★ Tablespoon

★ Cupcake cases

★ A baking tray

★ Clean hands!

1. Empty the crisped rice into a large bowl.

2. Ask a grown-up to place the cocoa, butter and honey in a small saucepan and stir over a low heat until melted.

3. While the mixture is melting, lay out 10 cupcake cases on a baking tray.

4. Ask a grown-up to pour the mixture into the bowl of crisped rice.

5. With a grown-up, stir it really well with the wooden spoon – be careful that the mixture doesn't fall out of the bowl!

6. Make sure all the crisped rice is coated in the gooey mixture.

7. With the help of a grown-up, spoon the mixture into the cupcake cases with a tablespoon.

8. Leave the crispy cakes to cool.

9. Once they are cooled they may be placed in the fridge to harden further or you can enjoy them straight away!

Why not try adding in some dried fruit or pieces of biscuit?
Or you could try using corn flakes instead of crisped rice. What's your favourite?

Odd Ones Out

These pictures of Fifi with Buttercup and Daisy all look the same, but only two are exactly alike. Can you tell which ones?

A.

B.

C.

D.

Colour Mo

Colour this picture of Mo and Fifi driving to Poppy's market stall.
What do you think they are going to buy?

Sleepover Surprise!

One day Bumble was helping himself to a drop of apple juice when Fifi Forget-Me-Not skipped by.

"Hello!" she called up happily. "You're just the bee I was looking for."

Bumble slid down the apple, landing on the ground in front of Fifi with a bump!

"What can I do for you Fifi?" he asked, picking himself back up again.

"Next Saturday Violet and Primrose are coming to my house for a sleepover," grinned Fifi. "Would you mind keeping an eye on Buttercup and Daisy?"

Bumble nodded. Buttercup and Daisy were still tiny Tots, and Fifi popped in to check on them every evening.

"I'll buzz over there at bedtime," suggested Bumble. "And you can enjoy your sleepover."

When Saturday finally arrived, Fifi put on her favourite denim pinafore dress.

"Primrose is always trying to get me to dress up smart," she chuckled.

"I'll wear this just for her!"

Next, Fifi set off to the market. She wanted to buy some scrummy sleepover snacks for her friends.

"Fifi! Fifi!" shouted the twins when she passed Buttercup and Daisy's house.

Buttercup tugged on Fifi's hand. "Can we come to your sleepover tonight?"

"Pleasssse," added Daisy.

"It will be too late for you two," smiled Fifi. "We'll have lots of sleepovers when you're bigger."

Poppy's market stall was packed with all kinds of delicious things to eat. Fifi stopped for an ice cream then pulled out her list.

"Please can I have three strawberries, some cream buns and a carton of milk?" asked Fifi, ticking everything off.

"Hee hee!" chuckled Poppy. "Sounds like you're going to have a lovely old time tonight."

Fifi nodded. "I hope so! Violet and Primrose are coming at six. Bumble's even promised to check on Buttercup and Daisy for me."

"Maybe he'll read them a nice bedtime story," replied Poppy, putting Fifi's shopping into a paper bag.

"Did you hear that bosss?" whispered Slugsy, sticking his head out of the grass behind Poppy's stall.

"Of course I did!" said Stingo, shushing him crossly.

The pair had been eyeing up Poppy's fresh strawberries before Fifi arrived. When the Tot had started talking about sleepovers they couldn't resist hanging around to hear some more.

Suddenly Stingo's eyes lit up. "If Violet and Primrose are going to Fifi's, that means Flowertot Cottage is going to be empty tonight!"

Slugsy scratched his head. "Ssso?"

"So..." snapped Stingo. "We can go round there and see what's in the kitchen!"

"Oh now that's better Fifi!" squealed Primrose, arriving for the sleepover.
"That dress is so much prettier than wellies and dungarees."
Fifi looked down and blushed happily, then showed her friends inside.
"I've packed my notepad and some colour pencils," smiled Violet.
"I thought I could draw you a picture."
"Thank you Violet," laughed Fifi.
"I'll fill the teapot and fetch some cakes."
Primrose put her bag on the
kitchen table and hugged both
of her friends. "Now isn't this fun?"

The sleepover turned out to be lots of fun indeed. Fifi, Violet and Primrose played dressing up, drew pictures, made friendship bracelets and shared heaps of giggles.

"Pyjama time!" called Primrose when it started getting dark outside.

Fifi pulled the curtains, then reached under her bed for her fluffy peach slippers.

"I do hope Buttercup and Daisy are OK," she whispered. "I normally pop over to Milk Bucket House around this time."

"Flutterby's always there," said Violet. "And you know you can count on Bumble to stop by."

Up on the veranda at Apple Tree House, Stingo and Slugsy were doing some serious spying.

"It's too dark bosss," grumbled Slugsy. "I can't sssee what'sss going on down there."

"Stingaling!" answered Stingo. "Give me the telescope."

Stingo swiped the eyeglass, then leaned over the edge of the veranda. In the distance he could just make out the shape of Violet and Primrose's little marrow house.

"Yes!" he cried, punching the air. "The house is dark and that means..."

The wasp turned to Slugsy, but his poor right-hand-slug didn't have a clue.

Stingo shook his head. "Doh! It means that both the Tots are safely out of the way at Fifi's house!"

Slugsy grinned nervously. "Let'sss go!"

When the sun finally set over Bumble's house, the kind bee buzzed inside to check the time.

"Seven o'clock," he announced. "I should be getting over to Buttercup and Daisy's."

Bumble's wings flitted and flapped as he slowly made his way across Flowertot Garden. When the bee buzzed past Violet and Primrose's house, something made him bump back down to the ground.

"Why are the windows bright?" he wondered. Primrose and Violet always switched the lights off when they went out.

Bumble looked up at the darkening sky. He had just enough time to take a quick peep inside.

Inside Flowertot Cottage, silly Stingo and Slugsy were having some sleepover fun of their own.

"Look at the size of this lolly!" cackled Stingo, helping himself to Violet and Primrose's larder. "There's cakes in here too!"

Slugsy looked worried. "I love yummy ssscrummy lollipopsss bosss," he replied. "But thessse don't belong to usss!"

Stingo just laughed. "Violet and Primrose are having a great time at Fifi's – they won't mind!"

"Oh yes they will!" shouted a cross voice.

Stingo and Slugsy both gasped. Bumble was standing at the front door.

"Wh-what are you doing here B-b-bumble?" asked Stingo, putting down a tray of cakes.

"I was going to check on the twins," replied the angry bee. "Looks like I should have checked on you too."

Slugsy hung his head in shame. "Sssorry Bumble."

"No good saying sorry to me," frowned Bumble. "I'm taking you over to Fifi's house. That way you can tell Violet and Primrose exactly what you were up to."

"We're in big trouble!" gulped Stingo.

Bumble and the naughty Tots marched over to Fifi's house. Just before they got to the front door of Forget-Me-Not Cottage, Flutterby glided into the garden. He lowered his wings so that Buttercup and Daisy could slide off his back.

"Hello!" said Bumble. "Shouldn't you two be in bed?"

The twins scampered over to meet their friend.

"You seemed to be running late," began Daisy.

Buttercup looked curiously at Stingo and Slugsy. "... so we wondered if you needed our help!"

Bumble smiled at the sweet pair. "I did get a little delayed," he told them. "Come into Fifi's and I'll tell you all about it!"

Stingo shook his head. "I'm not looking forward to this!"

Fifi ran to the front door. She was very surprised to see Bumble, Stingo, Slugsy, Buttercup and Daisy standing outside!

There were lots of surprised faces when Bumble explained what had happened.

"You must never go into someone's house without being invited first!" tutted Primrose.

"I know," answered Stingo. "And I'm very sorry."

"We've been very sssilly," added Slugsy.

Fifi found some extra pillows and blankets.

"Now that you're all here," she decided, "you'd better join the sleepover!"

The upset was soon forgotten. As the moon and stars filled the sky, Flowertot Garden echoed to the sound of singing, giggles and lots of fun.

See-saw Puzzle

How many of the pictures below can you find in this image of Fifi and her friends on the see-saw? Put a tick by the pictures that are shown in the larger scene.

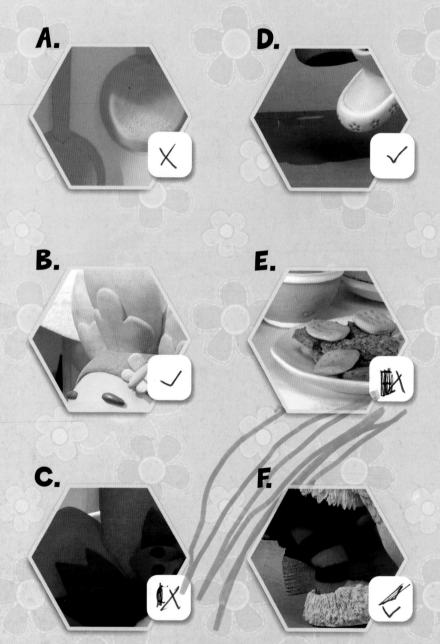

A. ✗

D. ✓

B. ✓

E. ✗

C. ✗

F. ✓

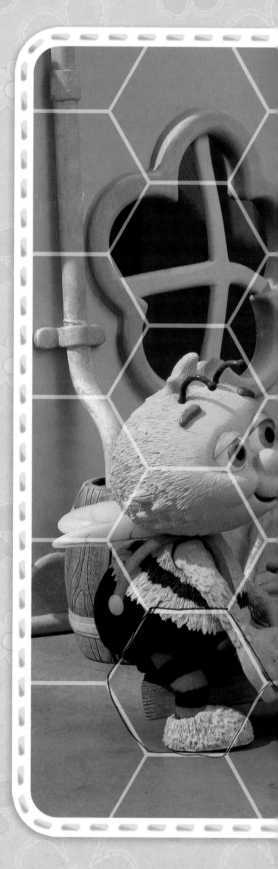

Copy Bumble

Draw a picture of Bumble in the grid, using the picture below as a guide.

Webby Tidies Up

Webby is sorting out her things. To help her, count how many of each object you can see in the picture.

There are ☐ pink flowers
There are ☐ paintbrushes
There are ☐ jars

Fun in the Garden

Your garden or the park are full of fun just like Flowertot Garden.
Fifi loves to grow things and to enjoy the natural world around her.
Why not try some of these great outdoor activities?
Remember: Always wash your hands after playing outside.
Always ask a grown-up before going outside.

Buttercups and Daisies

Flowers come in lots of different colours. How many flowers of each colour can you see in your garden? If there aren't any flowers in your garden, why not try the park?

Red ☐ Purple ☐
Orange ☐ Pink ☐
Yellow ☐ Blue ☐

Creepy-Crawly Hunt

There are lots of little creatures that live in the garden. Why not go on a creepy-crawly hunt and see what you can find? Tick them off as you go.

Can you see...
A butterfly like Flutterby? ☐
A worm like Diggly? ☐
A caterpillar like Grubby? ☐
A spider like Webby? ☐
A slug like Slugsy? ☐

Grow Your Own

Why not grow some plants like Fifi?

Remember: plants take time to grow and need lots of sunlight and water.

I. Take an empty margarine or ice cream tub and ask a grown-up to make some little holes in the bottom. When you water your little garden these holes will let it drain.

2. Put some soil in the tub – make sure you leave some space at the top.

3. Pour some water into an empty yoghurt pot and push it into the soil to make a little pond.

4. Plant some cress seeds in the soil. Use wooden lolly sticks to help remember where you planted your seeds and to check how they are growing. As they grow you can mark how tall they are on the lolly sticks.

5. Decorate your garden with leaves, stones, shells, feathers, flower petals or twigs.

6. Keep an eye on your cress to see how it grows! You can eat it in sandwiches if you like!

Spot the Differences

These images of Fifi and Bumble at Honeysuckle House look the same, but there are six differences in the picture on the right. Can you find them all?

Shadow Match

Can you draw lines to match each character to their coloured shadow?

A.

B.

C.

D.

1.

2.

3.

4.

Bouncing Bedtime

It's time to say goodnight, but Fifi and Primrose are having a pillow fight instead. Colour them in carefully – and decide who is going to win!

Answers

Page 08

Page 22

Page 23

A = 1, B = 3, C = 2

Page 27

Piece C is the missing piece.

Page 29

b	e	a	n	s	a	i	f	d
b	k	z	p	y	y	o	t	p
l	s	u	u	t	w	n	s	b
a	j	b	m	w	b	i	m	e
m	a	p	p	l	e	o	o	r
l	e	b	k	t	n	n	s	r
i	b	p	i	p	u	s	v	i
j	l	w	n	b	l	b	q	e
t	o	m	a	t	o	e	s	s

Page 33

A, C and G don't belong at a birthday party.

Page 36

Images A and D are exactly alike.

Page 50

Pictures B, D and F are shown in the larger scene.

Page 53

There are 4 pink flowers, 3 paintbrushes and 2 jars.

Page 56

Page 58

A = 3, B = 4, C = 2, D = 1